My Wonderful Aunt
Story Three

Did you ever hear tell
of my wonderful aunt?
She never said, "Won't!"
and she never said, "Can't!"

I heard a loud rumpus,
and to my surprise,
I discovered my aunt
selling wonderful pies.

3

Some people were buying
and others were looking —
For word gets around
when my auntie starts cooking.

And as for the line,
well, it ran from the till
Past the school and the dairy,
back over the hill.

5

There were very **big** pies
that would last you a week,
There were pies that were rugged,
and pies that were sleek.

There were pies made for frogs,
there were pies made for foxes,
And pies you could wind up
like musical boxes.

7

There were pies that exploded
with sparkles and smoke,
And a humorous pie
that would tell you a joke.

Did you hear the one about the rhubarb pie?

And there was my aunt
busy rolling and chopping
And mincing and tasting
and never once stopping,

Surrounded by crowds
of remarkable creatures
From ditches and deserts
and desolate beaches,

And all of them wanting
to get at the pies,
Whatever their color,
their shape and their size.

11

"Don't push!" said my aunt.
(She was kindly but stern.)
"Just stand in the line,
and you'll all get a turn."

"I don't want a rumpus,
a wrangle, a riot!"
And at once the whole crowd
grew peaceful and quiet.

There were toucans with tokens
and gangsters with gold,
A bear with a bike
and a king with a cold.

A dog with a drum
and a fox with a smile,
And a robot with wires
and a screen and a dial.

And all of them wanting
some sort of a pie,
Which they'd never
(no–never!) been able to buy.

17

So they frolicked and feasted
all over my lawn . . .
Hairy ones, scary ones,
shaven and shorn.

It was like a great picnic
that lasted all day,
While my wonderful aunt
kept on baking away.

But just as the stars
prickled out in the skies,
After giving three cheers
for my aunt (and her pies),

These very strange folk
disappeared down the street,
While shaking the gravy
and crumbs from their feet.

"I'm tired," said my aunt,
"now the pie-party's done,
But I **do** like a frolic.
I **do** enjoy fun."

"And I'll do it again,
very soon I'll be bound,
For when I start cooking,
the word gets around."

23